Dress-up
Alana
Doll

Cutting Alana out along the
dotted line will be tricky so
please ask an adult to help you.

Go to the back of the book to cut
out her fabulous outfits!

Arlene Phillips OBE is a world-renowned director
and choreographer creating musicals, videos, films,
television programming and spectaculars. Her
inventive choreography has been seen in the musicals
Grease, *We Will Rock You*, *Starlight Express*, *The Sound
of Music*, *Flashdance* and *The Wizard of Oz*. Her screen
work includes the films *Annie* and *Legend*, and the
television shows *DanceX* and *Britannia High*. Arlene's
videos have starred everyone from Robbie Williams
to Elton John, Whitney Houston to Tina Turner. Her
largest ever spectacular was the XVII Commonwealth
Games. She is known throughout the UK as a former
judge on *Strictly Come Dancing* and now on *So You
Think You Can Dance?* Her favourite job, however, has
been as mother to her two daughters, Alana and Abi.

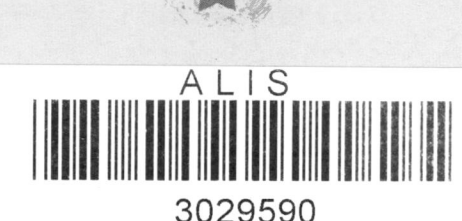

Typeset by Baobab Editorial and Design
Printed in England by Bookmarque, Croydon, UK

With thanks to Susan Reuben

A CIP record for this book
is available from the British Library

978–0–571–25991–5

2 4 6 8 10 9 7 5 3 1

LA Moves

By Arlene Phillips

Illustrated by Pixie Potts

faber and faber

Miss Trina

Keisha

Matthew

Verity

The Students at Step Out Studio

Alana

Meena

Chloe

Toby

*For Abi, who has always
inspired me*

Chapter 1

'And one-two-three, one-two-three, one-two-three . . .'

Alana and Meena spun round and round the classroom, concentrating hard on getting their steps right without crashing into the desks. They could hear the sound of shouting and laughing out in the playground, but today there was no time for hanging around outside with their friends. The Rosebury Primary school talent show was coming up and Alana and Meena were planning to perform the waltz that they'd learned at their dance class. It was over a year since they'd last done it, and they needed the practice, so they'd sneaked back inside when the teacher wasn't looking.

The girls had been having a lot of trouble getting the rise and fall right, but as they went through the steps over and over again, things started to come together at last.

'Sorted!' said Meena as the dance came to an end.

'Yeah!' said Alana. 'We were totally on it that time!' The girls gave each other a high five.

'Let's try it one more time before the others get back,' said Meena.

 2

But just as they started the dance again, Lara and Alice came into the classroom. They were sharing Alice's iPod, one earphone each, and singing along to the latest Girls Unlimited track:

You're my best friend, my soulmate,

Ooh ooh baby . . .

When they saw what Alana and Meena were doing, they started giggling, then clapped their hands over their mouths.

'What?' asked Alana defensively, not noticing she was treading on Meena's toes.

'Nothing!' said Lara, but she was obviously still trying not to laugh.

'Come on, guys,' said Meena, once she'd finished hopping around and moaning. 'What's your problem?'

'Well, it's just that . . .' began Alice, but then she started giggling again.

'. . . that sort of dancing isn't exactly

cool, is it?' Lara finished off for her. 'I suppose it's OK if you like that sort of thing. It just looks a bit like what my gran does at her social club on a Sunday afternoon.'

By this time, Alice had switched her iPod to the latest song by TJS. They were Alana and Meena's favourite band. Alana saw the four boys dancing on the tiny video screen and immediately forgot all about the argument she'd been having. 'Let's listen, too!' she said. So Alice switched her iPod on to loudspeaker, and the four girls sang along.

As the class started to file back in from break, some more kids joined in. A few crowded round the iPod and watched TJS on the screen, dancing their awesome hip hop routine. Others started jumping around to the thumping beat.

'Now *they're* cool!' shouted Lara above the sound of the music. Alana couldn't help but agree. Out of the corner of her eye, she noticed Toby, standing a bit apart from everyone else, but dancing too. Toby came to Step Out Studio, but he always said he hated dancing. He only went to dance classes because his mum made him – all he actually wanted to do was skateboard. So it was weird to see him now, dancing for fun. As soon as he noticed Alana watching him, he stopped abruptly and pretended to be absorbed by his skateboarding magazine.

Suddenly, a scary voice brought everyone to a standstill. Miss Walcott the form teacher was standing in the doorway, hands on hips. 'WHAT is going on here?' she yelled. 'Is this a classroom or a disco?'

Lara ran to turn off the music, and

when Miss Walcott silently held out
her hand, Alice gave her the iPod. Miss
Walcott locked it away in her desk drawer.

'A disco!' muttered Lara to Alana.
'Is Wally Walcott still living in the last
century?'

'She probably used to go to discos
when she was young, like, a hundred
years ago!' giggled Alana.

She didn't realise that the teacher had
come up right next to her. 'There seems
to be something amusing you, Alana,'
said Miss Walcott in a threatening voice.
'Perhaps you would like to stay behind
after school and tell me all about it? I
could do with some entertainment.'

'Erm, no thank you, Miss Walcott,' said
Alana meekly. Luckily, Miss Walcott let it

go. It was dance class straight after school and Alana would have been gutted to miss it.

The moment the bell rang for the end of the day, Alana and Meena dashed off to Step Out Studio. As they ran through the playground, they noticed Toby practising ollies on his skateboard. 'Uh-oh,' panted Meena. 'Toby's gonna be late for class again. Miss Trina will *not* be happy.'

Chapter 2

Miss Trina stood at the front of the class, her blonde hair shining, her elegant hands clasped together. 'OK, everyone,' she called, 'we're doing the foxtrot today. Find your partners please.'

Alana sighed. She usually had to partner Toby, but he hadn't arrived yet. Miss Trina spotted her looking glum. 'You can partner Matthew today,' she said.

'That's not fair!' cried a tall, slim girl.

'I'm always Matthew's partner!'

'Well, not today, Verity,' said Miss Trina smoothly. 'I'll dance with you today.'

Verity was the richest and the prettiest girl at Step Out Studio. Her parents very much liked the idea of her being Matthew's partner. He was a great dancer, *and* he was good-looking. His family was well off, like hers, and they went to the same private school. Most of the dance students couldn't care less how rich everyone's family was and what school they went to, but this kind of thing mattered a lot to Verity and her parents.

'Now,' said Miss Trina. 'Each couple is going to walk round the room until you move in perfect harmony. This is essential for a good foxtrot. After that, we'll work on the hold and the heel leads.'

As Alana and Matthew walked in time to the music, Verity kept shooting Alana horrible looks. Then, as they passed near each other, Verity 'accidentally' stepped on Alana's toe. Alana was wearing open-toed ballroom shoes, so she gave a yelp of pain.

'I'm *so* sorry, Alana,' said Verity, smiling sweetly at Matthew as she spoke. 'Of course, if you kept in time to the music, your feet wouldn't be in the wrong place for me to step on them.'

'Actually,' said Matthew, not smiling at all, 'Alana was perfectly in time.'

Verity's smile vanished in an instant.

'Thanks, Matthew,' murmured Alana, as they walked away.

After class, Alana and Meena were in the changing room, getting back into their everyday clothes, when Miss Trina came in to talk to them. 'How's the practice coming along for your school talent show?' she asked. 'I've always loved the waltz sequence you put together – I'm sure you'll do a good job of it. In fact, I'll be there to watch – my niece is going to be singing a solo.'

'We love our waltz, too,' said Alana. 'But I'm not sure any of the others will. They think ballroom dancing is totally uncool.'

Miss Trina sighed, and sat down on the bench next to the girls. 'Sometimes,' she said, 'you have to be prepared in life for people who don't appreciate the things that matter to you and that you love. You just have to go ahead and do them anyway.'

Alana and Meena looked at each other and raised their eyebrows. Miss Trina could see that her advice wasn't really helping.

'Tell you what,' she said, trying a different approach. 'You know, often the best way to make people change their

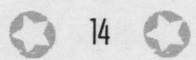

minds about something is to surprise them. Make them see it like they've never seen it before. That's always got a good chance of working.'

'But how?' asked Meena. 'What could we possibly do to stop everyone thinking the waltz is just a crusty old ballroom dance?'

'You're bound to come up with

something,' Miss Trina replied. 'What do all the kids in your class love? That could be a good starting point. Now, you'd better hurry up and get changed — it's getting late. Your parents will be here to collect you any minute.'

As Alana was putting on her jeans and trainers, she thought about what Miss Trina had said. 'What does everyone in my class love? Well, TJS of course. But so what? What has TJS got to do with ballroom dancing? Nothing. Oh — this is useless.'

Without realising it, she'd been singing along to the latest TJS single while she was thinking. Suddenly, Verity's voice broke into her daydream. 'Ugh, you're not singing a TJS song, are you? Their songs are SO awful and so is their dancing.'

'It is not!' said Meena, springing to Alana's defence.

'Street dancing is totally vulgar,' continued Verity as if no one had spoken. 'It's not proper dancing at all. You *would* be into them, you two.'

'You don't have to like them if you don't want to,' replied Alana calmly. 'But we love them. They won *Superstar Search*, you know.'

'*Exactly!*' replied Verity. 'My daddy says those television talent shows are just mindless entertainment for the masses. He says they're the last straw for civilisation.'

Alana didn't know what that meant, but she knew it was something rude. Just as she was about to argue back, Chloe popped her head round the row of lockers to join in the conversation.

'Ooh, are you talking about TJS?' she squeaked. 'I love them! They're so cool! Don't you just love them too, Verity?'

Chloe was the most unquenchably happy person that Alana had ever met. She was rather clumsy and not a great dance student, but she had such a sunny temperament that it never seemed to bother her.

'I'm sorry,' said Verity, pretending to look around her. 'Did somebody speak? I thought I heard a voice but I can only see a marshmallow.'

'It was me, Verity!' said Chloe, waving — as usual, totally failing to realise that Verity was being mean.

'Come on, Chloe,' said Alana, taking her by the arm and leading her away before Verity had a chance to say anything else. 'Let's go and see if anyone's here to pick us up yet.'

But Alana's mum hadn't arrived. As the students were collected one by one, there was still no sign of her. At last, only Alana and Meena were left.

'Are you sure you don't want a lift home with us?' said Meena, whose dad was just pulling up outside.

'Thanks,' said Alana. 'But Mum definitely promised that she'd be here. I'm sure she'll come any minute.'

Alana really didn't want to make a big deal of her mum forgetting to collect her. 'Oh look,' she said, pretending to point to a car in the distance. 'Here she is now.'

'OK, brilliant, see you tomorrow!' said Meena as she climbed in the back of her car.

Alana waited a bit longer, but her mum still didn't turn up. After half an hour, she set off to walk home, sighing.

As she walked, she thought some more about what Miss Trina had said. If her class loved TJS so much, then maybe she and Meena should be doing a TJS routine. But they'd never done street dancing before, and they didn't have the right clothes for it. And anyway, she wasn't sure that just copying a TJS routine was what Miss Trina had meant. What had she said? 'Make them see it like they've never seen it before.' And she was talking about their waltz, not about street dancing.

As Alana turned the corner on to the high street, it started to rain. She wished she was in a nice, warm car. 'Brilliant!'

she thought sarcastically, as she ducked
her head and started to run down the
pavement. 'Why can't I have a normal
mum who can remember to pick me up,
and doesn't work all the time, and doesn't
expect me to spend half my life looking
after my sister, and and and . . .'

She was so engrossed in her thoughts
that she didn't even notice where she
was till she spied a familiar glow out of
the corner of her eye. She was passing
Madame Coco's Costume Emporium,
the shop that had led to an extraordinary
adventure the last time she'd visited it.

Unlike all the other shops on the high
street with their neon lighting and ever-
changing window displays, Madame
Coco's window was always hung with

richly patterned cloths, completely hiding what was inside. The odd glow that had attracted Alana's attention was the only indication that the shop was open.

Alana hesitated, trying to decide whether to go in. The rain was getting heavy now, and Alana didn't have an umbrella. The shop looked cosy and inviting. And, thought Alana, it would be nice to say hello to Madame Coco and see if she had any good ideas about the talent show.

Chapter 3

The shop door creaked on its hinges
and Alana paused in the entrance. The
first thing she saw was Madame Coco
carefully folding up a pink tutu in tissue
paper for a tall lady with long, black,
shiny hair. As the lady thanked Madame
Coco and turned to leave, Alana gave a
little gasp. She looked just like Isabella
Starr, Alana's favourite ballet dancer. But
what would a famous prima ballerina

be doing in a costume shop on the high
street? Before Alana had a chance to take
a proper look at her, she'd walked past
her and was gone. Alana shook her head.
Couldn't have been, she said to herself.

'Aha!' cried Madame Coco, bustling
towards her with her jewellery jangling,
and folded her in a big hug. 'It's ma petite
Alana, come to visit me again. But why
are you shaking your head, ma chérie?
Tell Madame
Coco all your
problems.'

'It's true, I
do have a
problem,'
said
Alana, 'but

that's not why I was shaking my head. I was just wondering whether that lady was Isabella Starr — but it couldn't have been, of course!' She laughed, feeling a bit embarrassed.

'I never discuss the names of any of my customers,' Madame Coco replied, with a small wink. 'Now ma petite, come and sit down and tell me what is *truly* troubling you.'

Madame Coco ushered Alana to the pink velvet armchair in the corner and brought her some fresh orange juice in a crystal glass. Then she sat down opposite her, and Alana started to talk.

There was something about Madame Coco that made it incredibly easy to tell her what was on her mind. In between sips of orange juice, she explained all her worries about the school talent show. She told Madame Coco about the waltz, and how she knew the right steps, but she didn't know how to persuade her class that ballroom dances like the waltz could be fun. All they were really into were bands like TJS.

Madame Coco listened to the whole story without speaking. Then she got up from her chair. 'Wait there, ma chérie. I have something that may help.'

She disappeared to the very back of the shop and Alana could hear her rummaging through the dress rails. She's probably got some amazing ballroom dress, thought Alana. But it doesn't matter how gorgeous it is, I still don't think the

Rosebury Primary kids will like our waltz.

But when Madame Coco came back, she wasn't carrying a dress. She had a pair of red slouchy trousers, a white vest-top with silver sparkles, a white cap with a silver dollar sign on it, and the best pair of trainers Alana had ever seen, with flashes of neon yellow and blue. The clothes looked exactly like the style TJS wore.

'That's such a cool outfit,' said Alana. 'But I don't get what it has to do with my waltz problems.'

'Why don't you just try it on, ma petite?' replied Madame Coco.

'OK,' said Alana, happy to try on the great clothes, even if they couldn't help her with her dance. She disappeared into the dressing room to change. Once she'd put everything on, she stood in front of the tall mirrors. She looked ultra cool and at least two years older. None of her school friends would even recognise her, she thought, grinning to herself.

When she came back out, Madame Coco said, 'Wait one moment and I will do your hair.' Deftly she gathered Alana's rich brown hair into two loose plaits, then tied them with blue ribbons decorated with red lips.

'So this band that you and your friends like so much,' said Madame Coco. 'TBC their name is?'

'TJS,' corrected Alana.

'Yes, that is what I said,' said Madame

 29

Coco. 'Why don't you try out some of this street dancing style that they do?'

'But I don't know how,' Alana replied. 'I mean, I like messing around trying to copy their dance routines with my friends, but I don't know the proper moves and neither does Meena.'

'Just think about one of the group's videos and copy the choreography they do,' said Madame Coco.

Oh, Madame Coco, that's harder than you think, thought Alana, but she closed her eyes and pictured the TJS video that she'd been watching in the classroom that day. Humming along to herself, she started to do the same moves, keeping the beat in her head. And as she danced, she began to feel a whirling sensation, as

if the shop were spinning round her. Her skin began to tingle strangely, but she kept dancing. Then the ground seemed to disappear from under her. Once again, she heard Madame Coco's voice, growing fainter and fainter, saying, 'Remember, ma petite, when your good deed is done, the call of home will beckon. You will return home! You will return home!' Then she felt the hard sensation of concrete under her feet and the thumping rhythm of electric hip hop beats vibrating through her body.

Alana opened her eyes cautiously. She was in what looked like a vast warehouse, with bare floors, high ceilings and enormous steel girders and pillars. Dazzling spotlights beamed around,

blinding her every time they crossed her
path, and there were television cameras
everywhere. Alana was finding it hard
to take it all in. She wasn't sure she was
ready for another of Madame Coco's
adventures.

Just then, a group of teenagers strolled
past her, chatting in American accents.

Alana quickly hid behind a huge speaker. Peeping round to take a closer look, she was amazed to see the teenagers were all wearing outfits similar to her own. The girls had on slouchy trousers, black caps, and strappy vest-tops with silver logos. The boys wore baggy jeans and black hoodies. And they were all wearing fantastic trainers – the kind she and her friends could usually only dream about.

Alana jumped as she heard an American voice booming out, 'OK! Let's take it from the top!'

Immediately the teenagers stopped chatting and got into position. A song blasted out of the speakers and the teenagers started performing an amazing hip hop dance routine. Alana watched, awestruck. There were sudden changes of rhythm and great body moves with tricks and spins thrown in. Everything was sharp, punchy and totally together – even the complicated locking and popping moves. Alana had had enough dance training to see that these kids were seriously good.

Then, just when Alana thought things couldn't get any more incredible, the cameras spun round to focus on a group of four guys. They were singing and moving forward in time to the music, getting closer and closer . . .

Chapter 4

As Alana watched the four boys, her heart started thudding in her chest. It felt like it was beating as loud as the music from the speaker in front of her. Could it be . . . ? It couldn't be, could it . . . ? It was!

Alana clasped her hands to her mouth. It really was! It was TJS, right there in front of her! They looked so fit and so cool, it was unbelievable. In a flash, she understood what was happening. This must be the shoot for TJS's new video, and she was right there watching!

Alana stood there following every step of the dance, and moving her hips gently to the beat. But then, just after the music shifted to a slower section, the same American voice called out, 'Cut! Sorry, guys. It's just not working. Let's take a break. Back in ten!'

The teenagers wandered off, catching their breath. But Alana wasn't looking at them. She couldn't take her eyes off the four members of TJS – especially Max who was her absolute

favourite. They strolled over to a refreshment table, chatting, and took swigs of mineral water.

Then Alana nearly jumped out of her skin as she heard voices right on the other side of the loudspeaker she was hiding behind.

'This routine is awesome,' one of them was saying.

'Yeah,' replied the other one. 'Except for the slow section after the second bridge. The director's right that it's not working. I think they're gonna have to change the choreography.'

Just then, the director's voice called out, 'OK, back in positions!'

Alana could see that everyone was totally disciplined. As soon as the director spoke, the backing dancers stopped chatting and got ready for the next take. Even the TJS boys put their drinks down and moved straight back on to the dance floor.

Alana watched everyone go through the routine again, and again the director called 'Cut!' in exactly the same place. This happened four times in a row. Alana was so engrossed in what was going on that, without realising it, she'd crept further and further out from behind the speaker. After the fourth 'Cut!', she was watching Max chatting with one of his bandmates, when he looked up and their eyes met.

Horrified, she ducked back behind the speaker, but it was too late. She could hear steps coming towards her.

Chapter 5

Alana's heart beat faster and faster. What was going to happen to her? You couldn't just barge in on a shoot like this – she was going to be in so much trouble! And it wasn't even her fault! She was starting to wonder whether visiting Madame Coco's shop wasn't a bit *too* exciting.

But when Max appeared round the side of the big speaker, he was all smiles. 'Hey, girl!' he said. 'What are you doing hiding there?'

'Erm, watching?' said Alana, in a sort of squeak.

'Well, there's not much to see at the moment,' he replied. 'We've got a big problem we need fixing. Do you ever make up your own dance routines?'

'Well, yes, sometimes in my bedroom,' said Alana shyly.

'Maybe you can help, then,' he said.

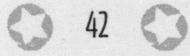

'We're having a nightmare here. We can't seem to get the routine down. It's the middle section that's not working.'

'I know the bit you mean,' said Alana. 'The director keeps getting you to do it over and over again.'

'Exactly,' said Max. 'We've come all the way to LA to shoot our new track with "the best in the business". But we've got to fly home tonight for a big concert, and at this rate, we're never gonna catch our flight. We can't let our fans down. Have you got any ideas?'

'Um, yeah, well . . .' stuttered Alana. 'It's a fantastic routine — I love it. But, well, yeah I suppose the middle is not quite, erm, as good as the rest?'

Max smiled and began to turn away.

Alana closed her eyes. Think, you idiot! she said to herself. Say something that doesn't sound completely dumb.

Just before Max was out of earshot, she blurted out, 'Maybe it's cos the music changes from a four-four to a three-four?'

'What? Yeah, I guess . . .' said Max slowly, turning back to her looking thoughtful.

'Well,' Alana continued, feeling a bit more confident, 'you see, if the beat is going one-two-three-four, one-two-three-four, and then suddenly it changes to one-two-three, one-two-three, it's maybe hard to keep the same dance style going?'

'You could be on to something, girl,' said Max. 'Maybe we need to try

something different in that section . . .
Hey, you seem to know your stuff! What
would *you* suggest?'

'Me?' said Alana, feeling shy again.
'Oh, er, I don't know *anything*. Honestly.
You don't need me! I mean, the only
dance I know in three–four time is the
waltz!' Alana cringed and turned red. She
couldn't believe what she'd just said. Here
was the coolest and most good-looking
guy on earth chatting to her, and all she
could talk about was the waltz!

'WHAT did you just say?' A young
woman with a pierced nose came
running up to her.

'This is Suki,' said Max. 'She's the
choreographer of our video. She makes
all the decisions about the dance routines.'

Alana could see that beneath Suki's make-up there were bags under her eyes and she was looking really tired.

'Suki,' said Max, 'this is . . .' Then he turned to Alana. 'Sorry – I haven't asked your name.'

'It's Alana,' said Alana, blushing. 'But just ignore what I was saying. It doesn't matter. Honestly. I'll just be over there – I won't disturb you again, promise.'

But Suki gripped Alana's arm, and looked at her intensely. 'Tell me what you were saying to Max!' she ordered.

'It was nothing. I was just saying that the only dance in three-four time I know is the waltz,' muttered Alana.

'The waltz,' said Suki to herself, closing her eyes and sinking into deep thought.

'That could be the answer! It's inspired!
Not a waltz as anyone would recognise it,
but an up-to-date version for the hip-hop
generation.'

'A revolutionised waltz, TJS style,' said
Max. 'Wow! Way to go, girl!' And he
high-fived Alana.

Suki ran up to the director, and Alana could see her talking to him and gesturing excitedly. The director was nodding. 'OK, everyone,' he called. 'We're gonna take a longer break. Back in forty-five please!'

'Cool, I'm starving,' said Max to Alana. 'I'm sick of the food we get given on the shoot – it all tastes the same. What d'you say we go out and grab something to eat from outside?'

'Erm . . . sure!' replied Alana.

'Hey, guys,' called Max. 'Let's go grab a bite to eat.'

The other three members of TJS came strolling over. 'This is Alana,' said Max. 'She's gonna join us.'

'Hey, how's it going, Alana?' said the boys.

'Erm, I'm very well, thank you,' Alana replied. I sound so stupid! she thought. She was so overwhelmed that she was about to have lunch with the whole of TJS, that it was quite surprising she was managing to speak at all!

The five of them went out of the warehouse into a brightly lit reception area, with framed platinum discs and photos of bands all over the walls. Only then did Alana realise that it wasn't a real warehouse – it was actually just a set in the middle of a film studio.

As they left the building and walked on to the blazing-hot streets of LA, the boys immediately pulled on baseball caps and sunglasses and hunched up their shoulders, staring at the ground as they went. 'Of course, they don't want to be recognised,' thought Alana.

She looked around her, squinting in the glaring sunshine. In front of them were rows of palm trees and wide pavements and, in the far distance, she could see a hill with the Hollywood sign on it.

They went into the first fast-food restaurant they came to: a Poppa's Pancake Paradise. 'What you having, Alana?' asked Max. Alana ordered a chicken pancake with sour cream and a bubblegum-flavoured milkshake topped with whipped cream and multi-coloured sprinkles. Max paid, luckily, as Alana didn't have any money at all, let alone dollars!

When everyone had got their food, they all went to a corner table and sat down.

Ramon, one of the band members said, 'So, Alana – tell us about yourself. What's your story?'

Immediately, Alana panicked. What was she going to say? How could she possibly explain who she was and how she'd come to be here? She didn't even understand the second bit herself!

She was just wondering whether to make a run for it, when a piercing scream echoed round the room. Three teenage girls came tottering over in high heels, crying, 'Wow! It really is! It's TJS! I can't believe it!'

Chapter 6

TJS glanced at each other in a resigned way – their disguise clearly hadn't been good enough. Then they smiled charmingly at the girls, and chatted to them and signed their autographs on their napkins. Of course, by this time the whole restaurant had realised what was going on and there was no hope of the group having a quiet lunch.

The band quickly finished their

pancakes, and they all set off at a run to be back at the studio in time.

'Is it always like this, wherever you go?' asked Alana, panting.

'Pretty much,' Max replied. 'But that's OK. I mean, we're lucky to have such great fans who like our music and our dancing. So if that means we don't get as much privacy as we want, that's just the way it goes.'

When they got on to the set, Suki was busy gathering all the backing dancers into the middle of the floor. The TJS boys went to join them, and Alana hid behind the loudspeaker again. She felt more comfortable there where people couldn't see her.

Suki started teaching everyone the

new steps for the middle section. Within twenty minutes, everyone knew what they were doing.

'OK, guys, into position!' shouted the director. 'And . . . action!'

Alana watched as the dancers did the now familiar steps. Then, when the music changed to three-four time, they danced the new choreography they'd just learned perfectly. The movements still had the same feel of the earlier section, only now they were more fluid with lots of body ripples and waves. Alana recognised some of the steps from the waltz she'd been

taught at Step Out Studio. It was weird, but somehow it worked.

This time the director let the song run right to the end without crying 'Cut'.

'I think that's a wrap, everyone,' he called. Then he looked over at Suki. 'Excellent work!' he said. 'You really turned that around.'

Alana saw Suki go over to him and whisper in his ear.

'Actually, people,' the director called, 'it seems there's someone else here who helped rescue the shoot. A girl called . . .'

Suki whispered in his ear again.

'. . . Alana,' he continued. 'Let's hear it for Alana! Come up here, Alana!'

Scarlet with embarrassment, Alana

crept out from her hiding place, to
applause from all the backing dancers
and from TJS.

Max came over and put his arm round
her, which made her feel a bit dizzy.
'What do you say, girl?' he said. 'I think
we should do the routine again for fun,
with you joining in this time.'

'Wow!' said Alana. 'I'd love to!'

'OK, let's do it, guys!' said the director.

Max got Alana to line up so there were two members of TJS on either side of her. As she waited for the cue, her heart was beating like mad and she was beginning to wish she hadn't agreed to do the routine. This is crazy, she thought to herself. I don't even know the basic street dancing moves. I'm going to look like such a loser.

But there wasn't much time for her to get nervous, because right then the director called, 'Action!', and the music began. Alana started dancing with

TJS right on cue, and she found to her amazement that she could keep up with their steps without any problem. And when they did some amazing break dancing moves, she discovered that, as if in a dream, she could do them too, like she'd been practising all her life.

As the song drew to a close, Alana could feel that her cheeks were still red, but this time with excitement and pride, not embarrassment.

'Thanks, Alana – you were wicked!' said Max, and he gave her a hug. As he did so, Alana felt him slip something into the back pocket of her slouchy trousers.

Then from

somewhere far in the distance, she heard
a familiar voice saying, 'When your
good deed is done, the call of home will
beckon. You will return home! You will
return home!'

Oh no she thought. I don't want this
adventure to end! But there was nothing
she could do. She felt a whirling sensation
in her head and the warehouse started
to lose focus. The ground disappeared
beneath her and the sounds of the
dancers grew fainter.

Then her feet touched the ground
again and she opened her eyes. She was
back in Madame Coco's shop. She was
standing in front of the floor-length
mirror. Looking at herself, she saw that
her cheeks were still pink, and her eyes

were bright with the excitement of what had just happened. Madame Coco was seated in a chair, smiling at her gently.

'Thanks, Madame Coco,' she said, running over and giving her a peck on the cheek. 'I'm going to get changed now. I've gotta run! I'm going to teach Meena the routine I've just learned, so we can do it at the school talent show!'

'I will pack up your dance clothes for you,' said Madame Coco.

'Can I really borrow them?' asked Alana.

'But of course,' said Madame Coco. 'You cannot do the hip hop in your waltzing ballgown!'

Chapter 7

As soon as Alana got home, she picked up the phone to call Meena. She told her that she'd found the answer to what they should do at the school talent show, but she wouldn't say any more over the phone. Ten minutes later, Meena was knocking on her front door. Alana hustled her up to her bedroom before her mum or her little sister Abi had a chance to ask what was going on.

'So?' asked Meena, as soon as the bedroom door was closed. 'Spill! I'm desperate to know!'

'I've got the answer! I've got the answer!' Alana sang, spinning round the room.

'Wait wait wait, stop!' said Meena, trying to get Alana to stand still.

'I can't stop! I'm too excited!' Alana replied, still spinning. Then she paused as she realised it was going to be incredibly hard to convince Meena to do the new TJS routine without telling her the secret of Madame Coco's shop. And if she were to tell her, Meena would never believe her. She'd think she was crazy.

'Erm – my idea is to do a waltzy kind of hip-hop,' she said, a bit hesitantly.

Meena looked confused.

'Actually, I mean a hip-hoppy kind of waltz,' Alana continued.

Meena sat down on Alana's bed, folded her arms and gave her a hard stare.

'OK, look,' said Alana, feeling a bit desperate. 'I'll show you.' She quickly put on Madame Coco's yellow and blue trainers.

'Where did you get *those*?' asked Meena, her eyes wide with envy and disbelief.

'Don't worry about that,' said Alana. 'Just watch.'

She danced out the routine she'd learned in LA, humming along as she went. 'Now,' she said, 'we want the music to change to three-four time in the middle, so we can do these moves.' She demonstrated the fluid, waving waltz steps she'd done with TJS. 'You see,' she said, 'it's still a waltz, but not like one anyone's seen before.'

'Wow, Alana!' said Meena. 'How did you learn to do that? How did you even think of it?'

'Erm, it just sort of popped into my head when I got back from dance class,' Alana replied. 'Anyway, do you like it?' she said. 'We'd better get practising. We're going to have a load of rehearsing to do if we're going to perform this in a week's time.'

It took Meena a while to learn the moves, but by the end of the evening she was really starting to get them.

That night as Alana lay in bed, staring at the big poster of TJS on her wall, she wondered what music they were going to use for their routine. They couldn't use the song TJS were singing in LA because it wasn't even released yet. 'What's the answer, Max?' she said, looking into the brown eyes of the boy on her poster.

Then she remembered that Miss Trina had

a mixing desk in her studio, so that she could make up tracks for her students' performances. Maybe she'd help them by mixing some old TJS tracks together to get the effect they needed.

Chapter 8

The next time they had a class at Step Out Studio, Alana and Meena hung behind afterwards and explained to Miss Trina what they were looking for. Miss Trina was happy to help. Meena had brought a CD of TJS's last album. Together, they took two different tracks – one in four-four time and one in three-four time, and mixed them into a new track that was just right for their routine.

Not as good as having their new single from LA, thought Alana, but definitely the next best thing.

Now there was the problem of what Meena was going to wear. Alana had her amazing outfit from Madame Coco's, but Meena needed something to match. Miss Trina solved part of that problem, too. She rooted around in the studio props room and found some baggy khaki trousers that fitted Meena perfectly.

'But what are you going to wear on top?' wondered Alana as they were gathering their things together in the changing room.

'It's OK – I've got a little white vest-top at home which should be fine,' Meena replied. 'It's the trainers I'm most worried about. Mine are from our local supermarket — they're rubbish.'

'Did you just say trainers?' said a voice from behind them. Alana and Meena nearly jumped out of their skins. They'd thought everyone else had gone home.

There was Chloe, sitting in front of the next row of lockers, getting changed out of her practice clothes.

'Yes,' said Meena. 'I don't have any proper trainers for the street-dance routine we want to do at the school talent show.'

'What size are you?' asked Chloe.

'Two' said Meena. 'Why?'

'That's just perfect!' squeaked Chloe. 'My mum can never remember what size my feet are, and she bought me some

trainers in the sales. They're black and

silver. I love them sooo much, but they're

way too small for me. They're size 2 and

my feet are size 3½. However much I try

to squeeze them on, I just can't do it!'

'But I couldn't wear your trainers,' said

Meena. 'Doesn't your mum want to take

them back to the shop?'

'Can't!' replied Chloe. 'She keeps trying

to make me wear them and they don't look new any more — she got them, like, weeks ago. It's OK — honestly — I'd love you to have them.'

'Wow, Chloe, you're a star!' said Meena, giving her a hug.

'I can't wait for the school talent show,' sighed Chloe. 'I'm playing my clarinet in the school band. And there's going to be loads of people from Step Out Studio there.'

'Yes,' said Alana. 'There's going to be

us three of course. And Toby's doing a skateboarding routine with his friends. And there's Miss Trina, who's coming to watch her niece. That's everyone, right?'

'And Verity!' said Chloe.

'WHAT?' cried Alana and Meena together.

'Verity!' Chloe said again, a bit more quietly. 'Why? Is that a problem?'

'Why is *Verity* coming?' asked Alana, sounding a bit hysterical. 'She doesn't even go to Rosebury Primary! She goes to Primula Prep.'

'I invited her,' said Chloe. 'Was that the wrong thing to do?'

Chloe always thought Verity was much nicer than she actually was.

Alana covered her head with her

hands, and Meena sighed. But Chloe was starting to look upset, so Meena put her arm round her. 'It doesn't matter,' she said, kindly. 'I'm sure everything will be fine.'

Alana and Meena practised their routine every single evening. Sometimes they went to Alana's house, and danced on the hard floor of her bedroom where she did all her dance practice. Sometimes they went to Meena's. Her bedroom had carpet, which wasn't as good, but her room was quite a lot bigger than Alana's, which made some of the spins and slides a bit easier.

The night before the school talent show, they were rehearsing at Meena's. 'Phew!' Meena said, as the track came to an end, and she pressed 'stop' on her pink CD player. 'I think we've got it sorted!'

'I bet TJS would like our routine,' said Alana.

'Can you imagine actually dancing with them?' sighed Meena, dreamily.

Alana just smiled.

Chapter 9

It was the evening of the talent show, and the school hall was filled with rows of seats for the audience. Verity was already in the front row, wearing a designer outfit, with her nails painted a perfect pale pink. She was messaging away on her phone and she had a slight smirk on her face. Alana wondered why she'd got there so early – the show wasn't due to start for another hour.

Alana and Meena went into the little room behind the stage that had been turned into a dressing room. It was chaos. There was a boy practising his juggling act, but the balls kept hitting people because there wasn't enough space. Different people were practising different songs, all at the same time, one girl was playing the violin, and there was even a gymnast trying to do a cartwheel, when there was hardly room to stand upright!

Alana and Meena were already dressed up in their street dancing gear. They'd done their hair in two loose plaits, like Alana's hair in LA. Alana was wearing her hair ribbons from Madame Coco with the red lips, and Meena had found some black and silver ribbons that matched Chloe's trainers. Alana was stretching and warming up as best she could in the tiny space, when suddenly she clapped her hand to her forehead. 'I've forgotten to give the teacher Miss Trina's CD, so she can put it on when it's our turn to dance,' she said.

'It's OK,' Meena replied. 'Don't worry, there's still plenty of time.'

Alana went over to her jacket pocket where she'd put the CD, and felt inside for it, but it wasn't there. Her jacket had loads of pockets – she must have put it in a different one. But the other pockets only held the usual mix of tissues, a packet of sweets, some hairslides – definitely no CD. In desperation, she pulled her coat off the peg, and prodded it all over, hoping to feel the thin round disc. Nothing.

The girls looked at each other in horror. Where could it be? What were they going to do? They couldn't dance their routine to any other song – they needed Miss Trina's special mix that had the time change in it.

Just then, Chloe came into the dressing room holding her clarinet. When she saw Alana and Meena, she came over to them, beaming. 'I'm so excited!' she said. 'Are you excited? I bet everyone's excited! I'm definitely completely, utterly butterly excited!' Then she noticed that the girls were looking gloomy. 'What's the matter?' she asked anxiously. 'You don't seem excited.'

'We've lost the CD that we're meant to be dancing to,' explained Alana.

'Oh no, that's terrible!' said Chloe, sympathetically. 'I was just telling Verity about the great mix that Miss Trina helped you do, and . . .'

'Hang on,' interrupted Alana. 'Did you say you told *Verity* about our CD?'

'Well, yes . . .' said Chloe, a bit more hesitantly. 'She was in the dressing room earlier and I was chatting to her about it. Why?'

Alana and Meena groaned in chorus. 'Come on!' said Alana, pulling Meena out of the dressing room. 'I *bet* Verity has taken it. That would be just the sort of thing

she'd do. We've got to find out what she's
done with it!'

The girls ran out, leaving Chloe
standing there, looking confused.

'Maybe we should just ask Verity straight
out if she's got it,' said Meena.

'She's never going to tell us,' said Alana
miserably.

'Well, probably not, but it's worth a try.'

So Alana and Meena went over to where Verity was sitting in the hall. She was whispering something to her mum, who was laughing in a high, tinkly voice.

'Hi, Verity,' said Alana.

'Hello,' replied Verity, with a fake looking smile. 'Shouldn't you both be warming up for the talent show? I've heard you've got something very *modern* to show us all.'

'Well, we would be,' replied Meena, 'but we've lost the CD with the TJS mix we're planning to dance to. We wondered whether you'd seen it, because I know you were in the dressing room earlier.'

'Why would I have seen it?' asked Verity calmly, looking Meena straight in the eye. 'I wouldn't touch a TJS CD

– I can't bear them.'

'Come on, Meena,' said Alana, pulling her by the elbow. 'There's no point. We're just going to have to try and find it.'

'Good luck, girls,' said Verity, her lips curled up slightly at the corners.

'I'm *sure* it was her,' said Alana once they were out of earshot. 'I could see it in her eyes. But we can't prove it.'

'She's *always* doing mean things,' muttered Meena. 'Especially to you, Alana. I think it's because you're such a good dancer and she's jealous. And she probably feels even more annoyed now, because you got to be Matthew's partner.'

'Let's see if she's chucked it in one of the bins,' said Meena.

There was a row of rubbish bins in a

bricked-off section by the back door of the school. Alana lifted up the lid of the first one she came to, and immediately gave a cry. There was the CD, right on top.

Except it was no longer in one piece — it

had been snapped in half.

The girls sat on the ground by the bins, 'It's just not fair,' Alana said, her voice a bit shaky. 'After all we've been through to get this dance ready.'

'Come on,' said Meena. 'We may as well go back into school or people will be wondering where we are.'

They started to walk back slowly, Alana in the lead.

'What's that in your back pocket?' asked Meena. 'It's making your trousers look all wonky.'

'Dunno,' said Alana, feeling in the pocket of her slouchy trousers. Her fingers met something hard and shiny. Her eyes widened as she looked at it. It was a CD. Scrawled across it in black marker pen, were the words, 'A special track for a special dancing star! For Alana, love Max xxx'.

Alana remembered now that she'd felt Max slip something into her pocket

before she found herself back at Madame
Coco's.

'Let's go, Meena,' she said, her eyes
sparkling. 'I think everything's going to be
OK after all.'

Chapter 10

Alana grabbed a bewildered Meena by
the hand, and ran into the school hall.
'Trust me, this is going to work,' she said.
Then she asked the teacher to put the CD
on with the sound turned low, so she could
check what was on it. She only needed
to hear the opening notes to be sure – it
was a recording of TJS's brand-new song.
No one else in the world had heard it yet!
Alana leaned over and pressed 'stop'. 'This

is definitely the CD we want,' she told the teacher. She could see Verity looking over at her with a worried frown, but she hadn't worked out what was going on.

She soon would!

The girls waited in the wings for their turn. They were the last act before the interval. They peeped out into the audience of parents, grandparents, brothers and sisters, aunts and uncles. There was Meena's whole family. Her mum and dad were trying to stop her little brother and sister from

bashing each other with their concert programmes. Alana's mum and sister weren't there. Her mum was doing a late shift at the restaurant where she worked. Alana sighed, but then she pulled herself together — nothing was going to spoil her evening now.

The show began. A group of girls from Year 6 did a gymnastics routine and the school band played a medley of songs from the musicals — a little bit out of tune. Then Lara and Alice came up to do their Girls Unlimited number. Alana and Meena's classes with Miss Trina meant they were really quite good at judging people's dancing, and they could see that the girls hadn't rehearsed properly. In the sections where they should have been performing identical moves, Lara was always a beat behind. They still got a big round of applause, though.

At last, it was Alana and Meena's turn. As soon as they ran on stage and TJS sang the opening line of their song, there was a ripple of excitement round the room. Loads of the kids in the audience were TJS fans, but they'd never heard *this* song before – where had it come from? When Alana and Meena burst into their dance with a six-step down rock into a freeze, the audience went crazy. There was whooping and cheering, and a lot of the kids stood up and started dancing along. Halfway through, Alana was vaguely aware of Verity and her mother stomping out of the hall.

When it came to the middle section, the audience cheered even louder! Then Alana saw her mum and Abi, jumping around right at the front. Mum must have managed to get away from work early, she thought, joyfully.

As the song drew to a close there were cries of 'Again! Again!' But there wasn't time for more. The curtain fell and the lights in the hall went up. Some of the pupils brought out trays of orange squash and custard creams.

In the dressing room, Alana and Meena gave each other a hug. 'That was amazing!' said Toby, coming up with his skateboard under his arm. 'If we

did that kind of street dancing at Step
Out Studio it would be *much* less boring.'

'I could teach you the steps some time,
Toby,' said Meena, blushing a bit. 'If you
want, that is.'

'That'd be great,' said Toby.

'Wow!' said Lara, running up to them.
'That routine was awesome.'

'Yeah,' said Alice. 'I can't believe you managed all those tricky moves. I never knew you could do street dancing.'

'We couldn't till a couple of weeks ago!' said Meena.

'You must be so glad you didn't do that boring old dance you were practising before. The waltz, right?' laughed Lara.

'Actually,' Alana replied, 'what we did tonight was a kind of waltz. It was just a kind no one's ever seen before. Cool, huh?'

'Yeah!' replied Lara. 'That *is* pretty cool!'

As soon as Alana came back into the school hall, her mum rushed up to hug her. 'I'm so proud of you!' she said. Abi was just behind, bouncing up and down and squeaking with excitement. Alana picked her up and hugged her too. Then the three of them headed for home.

That evening, Alana sat on her bed with her legs crossed and took out the beautiful purple and gold album that Madame Coco had given her the first time she went to her shop. Opening it up, she slipped her TJS CD into one of the special pockets. Then she got out a gold and a silver pen, and decorated the outside of the pocket with stars and TJS logos.

Alana climbed into bed and lay there gazing at her TJS poster, lit up by the moonlight seeping round the edge of her curtains. She blew a kiss to Max, then, smiling to herself, drifted off to sleep.

Enter
Arlene's World
of Dance . . .

Become a street dance star!

Imagine you're dancing in LA, just like Alana and TJS. These special tips should help you perfect the best street dance moves!

★ Freeze ★

A freeze is a stylish, difficult and acrobatic pose.

Popping

Popping is the technique of contracting then relaxing the body muscles in order to cause a jerk.

Tutting

Tutting is a move influenced by Egyptian hieroglyphics. The arms are used to to create box shapes.

Fantastic street dance facts!

Street dance and hip hop developed on the streets of America in the 70s and 80s. They involve dance moves known as locking, popping, rolling, gliding, rippling and waving. They are performed to rap and R&B music.

Old School hip hop started in the 1970s and included street, funk and breakdancing.

New School dancing of the 1990s saw hip hop music develop new rhythms as styles became harder and more aggressive. Rather than bouncing and jumping, dancers used increased movement in the hips and pelvis to emphasise the backbeat.

New School hip hop is characterised by more starting and stopping, lacking the flow of Old School breakdancing.

Hip hop dancing has changed the world of dance, surpassing its street origins and finding a starring place in dance studios and schools.

Take a step further with Alana on her dancing adventures . . .

Collect all these fabulous stories!

Out now!

Book 1: Samba Spectacular

There's a big Latin show coming up at Step Out Studios. But Alana's samba isn't great and mum's forgotten to make her dress.

Madame Coco's Costume Emporium has just the outfit that Alana needs. And when she tries it on she's magically whisked off to Brazil to dance in an amazing carnival!

Will she learn the samba in time for the show?

Coming out January 2011!

Book 3: A Viennese Waltz

Alana is getting ready for the Ballroom Bonanza competition in London. But mum needs her to spend all her time babysitting, and now she's lost her partner.

Madame Coco has just the solution – a beautiful gown that magically transports her to the royal ballrooms of Vienna. Will Alana be able to dance with a prince and make it back to waltz her way to brilliance in the Ballroom Bonanza?

Book 4: Bollywood Dreams

Alana wants to help her best friend Meena audition for a brand new show, Bollywood Dreams. They both love Bollywood films, but they're not sure they've got the steps quite right.

Madame Coco knows just what to do! It's one short trip to her Costume Emporium before Alana is magically whisked off to the set of a fabulous new Bollywood film, dancing with beautiful movies stars and learning all the best steps to help make Meena a star too.

Coming out May 2011!

Book 5: Stage Sensation

Alana and her friends from Step Out Studio
are gearing up for a new performance in a show-
stopping musical. They all want to sing and dance
on stage, but some of them are finding the new
routines really hard.

Madame Coco's is the place to go! There, Alana is
transported to the bright lights of Broadway in New
York City where she meets the members of an amazing
dance troupe. Can she learn how to dazzle on stage
and help her friends become musical superstars?

Book 6: Twilight Tango

Alana faces her most difficult challenge yet – to
master the tricky tango. As she and her friends at
Step Out Studio struggle with the complicated
moves, their new show is suddenly put in jeopardy.

Madame Coco knows just what will help. Putting
on one of her stunning tango costumes, Alana is
magically whisked away to the backstreets of Buenos
Aires in Argentina where she is taught the passionate
story of the tango. Can she take all she has learned
back home to help her friends
dance a thrilling tango?

Dress-up *Alana doll* outfits!

Cutting these out along the dotted line and around the tabs will be tricky, so please ask an adult to help you.

Once cut out, fold the tabs around the doll.